CARTOON NETWORK™

£5.99

Mischief Match

Oh, Ms. Bellum? I need your help! I can't figure out which bad deeds were done by which villains. Can you please solve these equations for me? Once you have the numbers, then you can match the villain to their crime. Oh, Ms. Bellum, what would I do without you!

Crooks

Mojo Jojo	$(3 \times 133) + 13$	= _____
Rowdyruff Boys	$(3 \times 133) - 1$	= _____
Fuzzy Lumpkins	$(3 \times 71) - 3$	= _____
Him	$(3 \times 100) \div 2$	= _____
Princess Morbucks	$(3 \times 100) + (3 \times 2)$	= _____
Gangreen Gang	$(3 \times 52) - (112 \div 2)$	= _____
Giant Mutant Fish	$(3 \times 55) + (3 \times 33) + 1$	= _____

Crimes

100	–	Destroyed Townsville
150	–	Blew up radio tower
210	–	Squashed a bus
265	–	Ate a taco stand
306	–	Robbed a bank
398	–	Tracked mud across the museum floor
412	–	Broke into the Jewellry Exchange

Answers: Mojo 412, Rowdyruff Boys 384, Fuzzy Lumpkins 210, Him 150, Princess Morbucks 306, Gangreen Gang 100, Giant Mutant Fish 285

THE CITY OF *TOWNSVILLE...*

...HAS A *SWEET TOOTH!*

AND NOBODY LOVES THAT *SWEET STUFF* MORE...

...THAN THE KIDS OF *POKEY OAKS!*

I'LL GIVE YOU THREE *APPLES* FOR YOUR *SUGAR LOAF!*

YUCK! FORGET IT!

SCOUT COUP

JENNIFER MOORE &
SEAN CAROLAN—WRITERS
RICARDO GARCIA FUENTES—PENCILLER
MIKE DECARLO—INKER
JENNA GARCIA—LETTERER
DAVE TANGUAY—COLORIST
HARVEY RICHARDS—ASST. EDITOR
JOAN HILTY—EDITOR

POWERPUFF GIRLS CREATED BY CRAIG McCRACKEN

THE POWERPUFF GIRLS 26. June, 2002. Published monthly by DC Comics, 1700 Broadway, New York, NY 10019. POSTMASTER: Send address changes to THE POWERPUFF GIRLS, DC Comics Subscriptions, P.O. Box 0528, Baldwin, NY 11510. Annual subscription rate $23.88. Canadian subscribers must add $12.00 for postage and GST. GST # is R125921072. All foreign countries must add $12.00 for postage. U.S. funds only. Copyright © 2002 Cartoon Network. All Rights Reserved. CARTOON NETWORK, the logo, POWERPUFF GIRLS and all related characters and elements are trademarks of Cartoon Network. The stories, characters and incidents mentioned in this magazine are entirely fictional. Printed on recyclable paper. DC Comics does not read or accept unsolicited submissions of ideas, stories or artwork.
Printed in Canada.

DC Comics. A division of Warner Bros.—An AOL Time Warner Company

SO YOU SEE, PROFESSOR...

IF WE JOIN THE *MUFFIN SCOUTS*, WE'LL LEARN IMPORTANT STUFF!

AND WE GET NEAT UNIFORMS!

AND COOKIES!

I DON'T KNOW...IT'S AN AWFULLY BIG RESPONSIBILITY TO TAKE ON, WHAT WITH YOUR SCHOOLWORK, AND *SAVING TOWNSVILLE*...

THINK OF THE *CHARACTER* WE'LL BUILD!

THE *OUTFITS* WE'LL WEAR!

THE *COOKIES* WE'LL EAT--UH-- *SELL!!*

PLEEEEEEASE?

WELL...

OKAY, KIDS! LET'S WELCOME OUR THREE NEWEST BLUEBERRIES TO OUR HAPPY MUFFIN SCOUT BUNCH...

BLOSSOM, BUBBLES, AND BUTTERCUP!

HI!

HI!

HI!

NOW LET'S ASSIGN COOKIE DUTY FOR THE WEEK.

ME! ME ME ME!

EXCUSE ME, MUFFIN MOM...

WHAT IS IT, SWEETIE?

ACCORDING TO PAGE 56 OF THE MUFFIN SCOUT MANUAL, A SCOUT IS REQUIRED TO EARN SEVERAL MUFFIN BADGES BEFORE THEY ARE ELIGIBLE FOR COOKIE DUTY!

WHY, YOU'RE RIGHT, DEAR!

IT SAYS YOU HAVE TO EARN THREE OF THEM...

...THE KNOT TYING, ANIMAL HUSBANDRY, AND FIX-IT BADGES!

13

LATER...

GIRLS! *WHERE* HAVE YOU *BEEN*?!

SELLING COOKIES!

THE *HOTLINE'S* BEEN *RINGING* OFF THE HOOK! THERE'S BEEN A STRING OF *ROBBERIES* ALL OVER TOWNSVILLE!

TOWNSVILLE *BANK*...

⇒*GASP!*⇐

...TOWNSVILLE *JEWELRY* STORE...

WHAT?!

...AND THE *MAYOR'S* OFFICE!

⇒*BURP!*⇐

BLOSSOM, WE WERE *AT* ALL THOSE PLACES!

EVERYONE WAS PAYING ATTENTION TO THE COOKIES INSTEAD OF THE *CROOK!*

BUT WHO WOULD KNOW WE WERE THERE, *EXCEPT*...

LOOKS LIKE *YOUR* HAND'S BEEN *CAUGHT* IN THE *COOKIE JAR*...

...MUFFIN MOM!

YOU'RE COMING WITH US, COOKIE CROOK...

...AND *DON'T* TRY ANYTHING *CRUMBY!*

NOT UNTIL YOU'VE SEEN MY *HAT TRICK!*

SEDUSA?!

THE ONE AND ONLY! AND YOU *BRATS* ARE IN FOR...

...SOME SERIOUS DIS-*TRESS!*

whp CRAK

NNGH!

WHAT ARE WE GONNA *DO,* BLOSSOM?

KNOT TO WORRY, GIRLS...

A MUFFIN SCOUT IS *ALWAYS* PREPARED!

KNOT TYING

I WANNA GO SURFING!

COW AND CHICKEN
CREATED BY
DAVID FEISS

10TH ANNUAL SUNSHINE BEACH SANDCASTLE FESTIVAL

C'MON, KIDS, I NEED AN EARLY START TO WIN THIS YEAR'S PRIZE!

SON OF THE BEACH!

WRITER: *SUNBURNT MIKE KRAIGER*
ARTIST: *TAN TIM HARKINS*
LETTERER: *SURFIN' PHIL FELIX*
COLORIST: *SANDY DAVE TANSUAY*
ASST EDITOR: *HEATSTROKE HARVEY RICHARDS*
EDITORS: *KOOKY KEVIN DOOLEY*
and *DAFFY DANA KURTIN*

REMEMBER, CHICKEN, I'M GOING TO BE SUPPORTING YOUR FATHER'S EFFORTS ALL DAY, SO KEEP A CLOSE EYE ON YOUR LITTLE SISTER.

WHUT ABOUT MY FAR EYE?

STAY CLOSE TO THE SHORE, KIDS! THE SHARKS LIKE TO FEED FURTHER OUT. A-HEH-HEH!

SHARKS...?

COOL.

C'MON, CHICKEN! LET'S GO PLAY!

OOF!

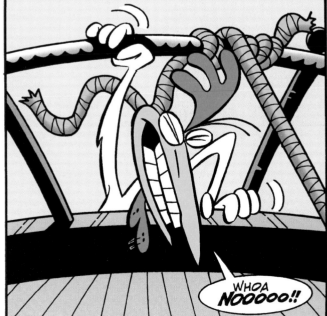

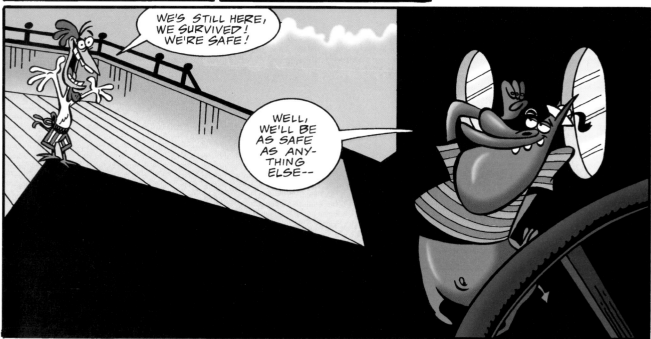

23

FRANK STROM &
DANNY ANTONUCCI-
WRITERS
SCOTT UNDERWOOD-
PENCILLER
ANGUS BUNGAY-
INKER
RYAN CLINE-
LETTERER
DIGITAL CHAMELEON-
COLORIST
HARVEY RICHARDS-
ASST EDITOR
JOAN HILTY-
EDITOR
ED ED & EDDY CREATED BY
DANNY ANTONUCCI

27

IT SEEMS WE'RE SHORT *ONE* BOARD.

BOARD, SHMOARD! WHO CARES? WE'RE GONNA BE *RICH!*

LIKE GRAVY?

UNLIKE YOU, EDDY, I FEEL AN INCOMPLETE PROJECT IS A *BLEMISH* ON THE FACE OF INTEGRITY.

FORGET ABOUT IT, DOUBLE-DEE. IT WON'T MAKE ANY DIFFERENCE.

SOON...

NEED I REMIND YOU THAT WE'RE STILL ONE BOARD SHORT, EDDY?!

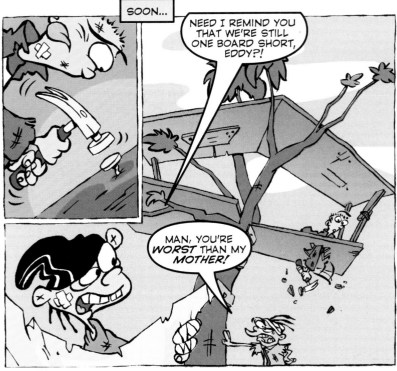

MAN, YOU'RE *WORST* THAN MY *MOTHER!*

...UNDERESTIMATE THE PO... ...F ENGINEERING EDDY. W... ...HAT TIMBER MISTER, ...EANHOWMANYTIMES ...TA...FFI...

ALL RIGHT ALREADY, WE'LL LOOK FOR A STUPID BOARD...*GEEZ*...

I Am Weasel's Wonky Words

Baboon, a significant amount of the time even I, Weasel, am unable to comprehend precisely what you are saying. Speaking clearly is key to successful communication with others. Unfortunately, my good sir, you do not share in my philosophy or my precise speech patterns. As a licensed speech therapist, I advise you to try these twisters to tighten your tongue.

Repeat each phrase at least five times, and say them as fast as you can.

• A bowl of blueberries for breakfast is a brilliant beginning.

I.R. eating bananas and berries.

• Baboon's big behind beams brightly on a beach in Brazil.

I.R. not in Brazil. I.R. staying here.

• Baboon babbles better than bird-brained bipeds.

I.R. better than Weasel.

Who said that there's nothing more boring than dancing with your sister? Breaking with tradition, Chicken assures us that no other couple has more rhythm and is in better sync than he and his sister, Cow. Now all of you can be Lords of the Dance with

COW and CHICKEN™

MACARENA

1 Raise your right hand...

2 Now raise your left hand...

3 Put your right hand behind your head...

4 Do the same with your left hand...

5 Lower your right hand to your hip...

6 Lower your other hand until you are in this silly position...

7 Jump while spinning around 90° and when you land, shout, "OOOOOAAA!!!"

39

41

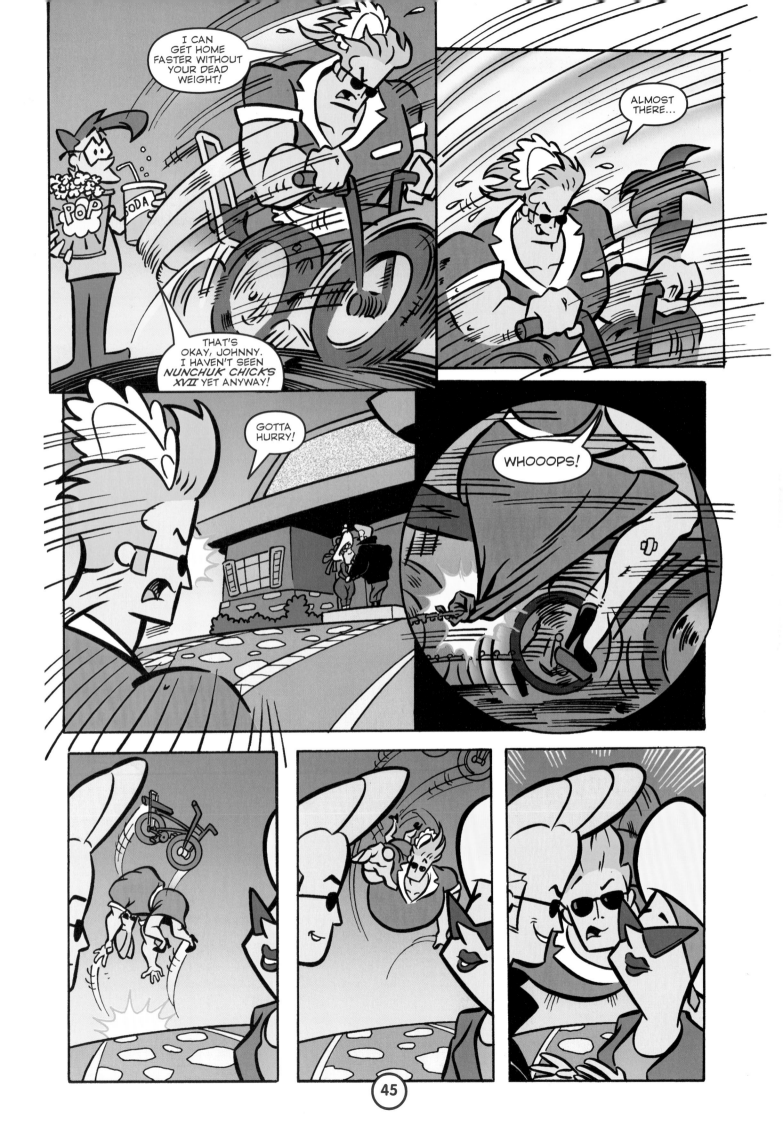

DEXTER'S LABORATORY 29. June, 2002. Published monthly by DC Comics, 1700 Broadway, New York, NY 10019. POSTMASTER: Send address changes to DEXTER'S LABORATORY, DC Comics Subscriptions, P.O. Box 0528, Baldwin, NY 11510. Annual subscription rate $23.88. Canadian subscribers must add $12.00 for postage and GST. GST # is R125921072. All foreign countries must add $12.00 for postage. U.S. funds only. Copyright © 2002 Cartoon Network. All Rights Reserved. CARTOON NETWORK, the logo, DEXTER'S LABORATORY and all related characters and elements are trademarks of Cartoon Network. The stories, characters and incidents mentioned in this magazine are entirely fictional. Printed on recyclable paper. DC Comics does not read or accept unsolicited submissions of ideas, stories or artwork.
Printed in Canada.

DC Comics. A division of Warner Bros.–An AOL Time Warner Company

TOOTH DELAY

DENTAL REPORT: DEXTER HAS A **CAVITY**

BOBBI JG WEISS – WRITER
MATT JENKINS – PENCILLER
JEFF ALBRECHT – INKER
WILDSTORM – LETTERER
ZYLONOL – COLORIST
HARVEY RICHARDS – ASST. EDITOR
JOAN HILTY – EDITOR

DEXTER'S LABORATORY CREATED BY GENNDY TARTAKOVSKY

FWIP-FWAP-WHAP!

AND THAT MUST BE THE SOUND OF—

FWIP-FWAP-WHAP!

—A HORI-VERTICAL LAP-STRAP PATIENT DEVICE—

—MADE ESPECIALLY FOR CHILDREN!

LUCKILY I NEVER LEAVE THE LAB WITHOUT MY HANDY GLOVE SNIPPERS!

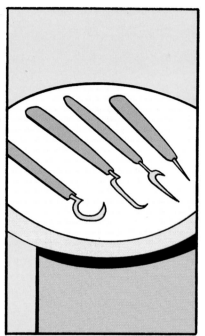

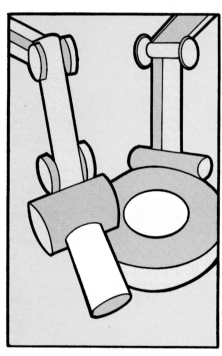

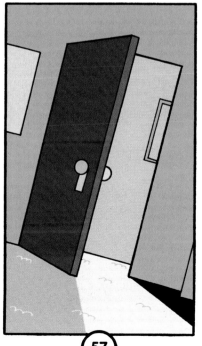

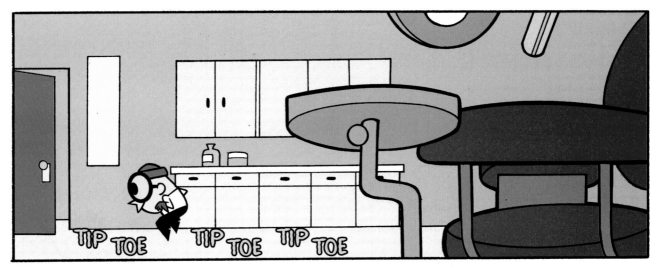